# Vitalis

D0104464

170,

# The Prague Golem

# The Prague Golem

## Jewish Stories of the Ghetto

Vitalis

© Vitalis, 2013
Produced in the European Union
All rights reserved

ISBN 978-80-7253-188-2

www.vitalis-verlag.com

# Contents

# How the Jews came to Bohemia

According to an old legend, at the time of the Second Temple[1], there was already a flourishing town in which Jews lived where Prague stands today. However, the town was later destroyed and the inhabitants driven away. Princess Libuše, who founded Prague in 730 AD, was generally known to be a prophetess. On her death-bed she called for her son Nezamysl and told him:

"I shall be at rest with my forefathers soon and before I go I want to reveal the future to you. When your grandson reigns over my people, a small foreign nation, rejected and oppressed, that worships only one God, will seek protection in our forests. May they be well received, may your grandson offer them protection for they will bring prosperity to the common land." When Hostivít[2] succeeded to the throne more than 100 years after the Princess had died, Libuše appeared to him in a dream and said: "The time has come for my prophecy to be fulfilled. A small, tormented nation that worships only one God shall come to your throne seeking help. May you receive them affably, hospitably and mercifully, and may you offer them protection and shelter."

After the Wends[3] wreaked havoc upon the Lithuanians and Muscovites, drove the inhabitants away, conquered the land and chose it as their seat, a Jewish community was evicted from the Muscovite area. Those miserable, unfortunate people roamed the world without shelter for ten years; eventually they reached Bohemia exhausted from their wandering. They asked for an audience with the ruler, the Prince Hostivít. Their request was granted. They were told to send two of their elders to the Prince. The Prince received them cordially and

---

[1] An era of Jewish history (circa 300 BC – 100 AD) which ended with the destruction of the Second Temple of Jerusalem in 70 AD
[2] Hostivít (died about 870 AD): legendary Bohemian Prince
[3] Wends: earlier general term for the Slavs

asked: "Who are you and what is your request?" The delegates replied: "We are a small nation and we call ourselves after our progenitor – Israel. We lived peacefully in one of the provinces in the Muscovite area until a powerful enemy came, conquered the land and drove its inhabitants away. We have wandered restlessly through the far wide world; the moorland was our bed, stones were our pillows and the heavens our roof. We are a peace-loving nation, small in number and lacking in strength. We follow the teaching of Moses; we worship one God who is almighty, omniscient, all-righteous and all-embracing, whose glory fills the whole globe. We humbly beseech you, O Prince, that it might please you to let us build our dwellings here. Give us your mighty protection, O Prince, that we may be your loyal subjects and beseech our God to grant

View of the Old-New Synagogue and the Jewish Town Hall in Prague

glory and victory to you and your people." Immediately the Prince recognized that this was the nation whose arrival had been prophesied. But he said wisely: "You shall receive your answer in two days. Come to see me the day after tomorrow and I shall tell you if I can grant your request."

On the morning of the next day he assembled all the *Vladykes*[4] and said: "My ancestress Libuše prophesied before she died that a nation seeking for help would come to our land. When I succeeded to the throne, Libuše appeared to me in a dream to tell me that the time would soon come for her prophecy to be fulfilled. She also told me that I should support these oppressed people who worship only one God and give them protection. And see, two elderly members of such a community approached me yesterday. They belong to the ancient and venerable Jewish nation. They have asked for permission to settle in our forests and there is no doubt that these are the people described by my ancestress. I would like to give them a place to settle in our country because they will bring us good fortune and their blessing. I shall send for them tomorrow because I would like to hear your views first."

"Do as was said!" the assembly replied. "Libuše said, that these people will bring us prosperity and give us their blessing."

The Prince gave the Jews a dispensation permitting them to settle on the left bank of the River Vltava in the environs of present-day Újezd[5]. The Jews kept the word they had given to the Prince. The oldest Bohemian chronicler, called Cosmas, describes how the Jews of Prague gave Prince Hostivít great support when at war with the Germans by supplying both provisions and finances so that he succeeded in expelling them from Bohemia.

So there were already Jews living in Bohemia in pagan times, long before the Christian faith became known there.

Under the reign of Bořivoj[6], who allowed himself to be baptized in 900 AD, the Jewish population had increased so much that the area they inhabited became too small for them. They asked the Prince for more space and were granted a site on the right bank of the River Vltava which is now Josefské město, previously known as the Jewish Town. A large area was given to the Jewish community and people who had little or no money were subsidized by the Prince to build their houses there. A large piece of ground near the Jewish Town was also given them for a cemetery. The construction of the Jewish Town began in 907 AD. Initially, it

---

[4] *Vladykes:* knights, landed gentry; the second aristocratic order under the Bohemian crown, below peers

[5] Újezd: an old settlement-area in Prague where Karmelitská Street is today

[6] Bořivoj I (died before 890 AD): the first baptised Bohemian Prince; the information concerning the year 900 AD does not coincide with historical facts

consisted only of thirty mostly wooden houses. Advanced architecture was not widespread in Bohemia at that time and for larger constructions master-builders from distant Italy would have had to be called in. Naturally this was possible only for the Prince and for some of the elite and nobles, such as the *Vladykes*. The first synagogue of the Prague Jewish community was therefore built of wood.

Since the Prague Jews came from the Muscovite area, they were attired in the "Russian" style and they had established the Polish rites in their synagogue which are still used in the Old-New Synagogue and sometimes in other smaller synagogues. The first Rabbi[7] of the Prague Jewish community was Malchi, a great scholar who was born in Cracow. The Jewish population continued to grow and remained under the protection of the rights granted them by the Prince. These rights were even extended on several occasions when the Jews performed exceptional deeds, such as in 1150 during the reign of King Vladislav[8], when a group of sectarians emerged. They called themselves flagellants and began to defame the prevalent religion, and the whole nation was tempted to convert. The King ordered all flagellants to leave Prague, and the country. Being too weak to oppose the King's will the flagellants then chose the Jews as victims of their revenge. One night the Jewish Town

was attacked, but the aggressors had made a mistake. The Jewish butchers, who were a large group at that time, had gathered at the first warning signal. Each holding a butcher's knife in one hand, and a burning torch in the other, they rushed towards the furious crowd, who, although greater in number, were panic-stricken and fled. However, the Jewish butchers chased them and drew them out of the town.

King Vladislav had the Jewish butchers summoned to praise them for their courageous behaviour, and he stressed how glad he was that they had protected the Jewish Town against the attack and chased the invaders away from the town. From then on, the Jewish butchers were allowed to bear the Czech double-tailed lion on their coat of arms as a reward. All subsequent Bohemian kings confirmed this privilege. King Vladislav also gave the Prague Jews the right to fortify the Jewish Town and to surround it with gates which were to be closed at night to prevent similar attacks.

From the time of Vladislav to that of George of Poděbrady[9] the Jews lived in undisturbed peace despite the serious upheavals that affected Bohemia. From then on, defamations against the Jews arose from time to time. On several occasions the Jews were expelled from the country only to be called back after

---

[7] Rabbi: 'My Master', the title of a wise man in the Mishnah period, a name for a Torah scholar or a Chasid leader

[8] Vladislav II (born circa 1110, died 1174): Bohemian Prince and King

[9] George of Poděbrady [in Czech: Jiří z Poděbrad] (born 1420, died 1471): an important Bohemian King

it was proved that these defamations had been inspired by the basest hatred. But the Jews fulfilled their duties loyally and were always quiet and unselfish Bohemian citizens. God who does not abandon the people of Israel, ... let them again find mercy before the monarchs of the land.

Interior of the Old-New Synagogue

# The Old-New Synagogue of Prague

With the exception of the synagogue at Worms, where a Jewish community was living at the time of the Second Temple, the Old-New Synagogue is the oldest preserved Jewish synagogue. The intact west wall of the Temple of Jerusalem, which has survived the ravages of time, can be considered no more than a ruin.

The Old-New Synagogue, preserved in Gothic-Germanic style, is typical of European medieval architecture, of which the most perfect examples are to be found in Germany. Three parts of the synagogue can be distinguished from the outside: the men's section, the women's section and a small chapel which is mostly used to hold services for those who are not allowed to visit the synagogue at the time of the general service. The two latter parts, and the women's section in particular seem, however, to be of a later date. The entrance is located on the southern side with short flight of steps leading downwards into the building.

The Prague Jewish community had increased so much that there was no longer enough room for all the believers in the first wooden synagogue. In the year 4690 after the creation of the world, which is 929 in the common Christian calendar, prominent members of the Prague Jewish community met and decided that a large stone synagogue should be built. A desolate hill covered with stones, undergrowth and half-rotten trees in the Jewish Town should be levelled and a new synagogue built there. When digging over the hill the workers discovered some completely intact walls made from blocks of white stone . They seemed to be walls of a former house of God. The supposition became a certainty when they found a Torah scroll made of deerskin and a few prayer books written in Hebrew.

At that time there were two delegates of the Jerusalem community in Prague, whose task it was to collect money to support the poor of the Holy City. They were men of great wisdom, with profound knowledge of the Talmud, and Rabbi Chisdai, who was a great Talmudic scholar in the Jewish community in Prague, asked them for advice about the building work. They were especially in doubt regarding what was to be done with the stones from the walls they had found. The two men from Jerusalem said: "Jews must have already been living here at the time of the Second Temple and they must have built this house of God. These stones have been consecrated once, and they are well preserved and are usable. They should be used for the new building. We also advise you to build this synagogue like the one in Tiberias, which was built after the plan of the Holy Temple of Jerusalem. You should therefore build 'schkufim atumim' windows, which means that the window openings should be wide at the outer wall and become narrower through the whole thickness of the wall to the inside. Two pillars should support a mighty vault and a few steps should lead down into the synagogue. The synagogue should be situated below the level of the surrounding landscape because it is said: 'I call to You from the depths, O Lord!' If you build the synagogue in this way, the Almighty shall listen to you at this place and He shall in his mercy protect this house of prayer against destruction by fire and water."

Not all members of the Jewish community were satisfied with this advice. Some thought it would be a violation of the memory of the Jerusalem Temple. However, when the prophet Elijah appeared in a dream to Sch'lomo Kun's, who was the head of the Jewish community, and told him to follow the advice of those men, everybody agreed. The two Palestinians left Prague loaded with rich donations for the poor of the Holy City. A Saxon architect by the name of Lirensky was engaged to carry out the construction of the synagogue. Building work proceeded quickly, and

Studying the Talmud

Life in the ghetto

the new synagogue was consecrated two years later, on Shavuoth[10] in 931 AD. The synagogue was called the Old-New Synagogue because the new synagogue was built from the stones of the old one.

No substantial changes have been made to the inside of the building since it was built, and over a thousand years its walls have turned deepest black. Because the name of God was written on the walls in several verses, they were never to be whitewashed. But for the Jews, this thousand-year-old dust represents their sacred past because the blood of their fathers clings to the walls. In the year 1388, under the reign of Wenceslas the Lazy,[11] a rioting crowd attacked the Jewish Town. The Jews must renounce their faith or die. The Jews were taken by surprise and too weak to resist the numerically superior mob. Old men, young men, women and children fled to the Old-New Synagogue. The furious crowd followed them and the door was broken open by force. None of them would renounce their faith and so they were all brutally massacred, children in front of their mothers, fathers in front of their sons. The blood of the martyrs splashed up onto the walls of the house of God.

King Wenceslas let the atrocity go unpunished and even without legal investigation. The case gave rise to great discontent among the country's elders and among most of the people as well. The never-ending excesses and outrageous cruelties of the King, who had had the Queen ripped to pieces by his hunting dogs, her confessor thrown into the River Vltava and many other respectable men of the land executed, aroused the people's wrath.

It is remarkable that the dignified building of the Old-New Synagogue survived intact the many fires that raged in the Jewish Town. During the fire in 1558 two white doves were seen on top of the synagogue. They flew up and disappeared into the clouds after the fire had been completely extinguished – when the Old-New Synagogue no longer needed special protection.

More than sixty curtains for the Holy Ark[12], richly decorated with gold and pearls, are kept in the synagogue. One of them is a donation from Karpel Sachs, the first Parneß[13] of the Prague Jewish community, dating from 1601. Another one came from the well-known Jekew Schmiles and his wife who ran their own mint in the Jewish Town on the square that was then called Dreibrunnenplatz.

---

[10] Shavuoth: a two-day holiday; one of three Pilgrim festivals of the Hebrew year; the giving of the Law to Moses on Mount Sinai is commemorated during this feast. It is identical with the Christian Whitsun feast

[11] Wenceslas IV [in Czech: Václav] (died 1419): Bohemian king, Holy Roman Emperor; the son of the legendary Charles IV

[12] Holy Ark; a case in the synagogue which serves for keeping the Torah scrolls; it is a most holy relic

[13] Parneß: the chief representative of the Jewish community

Title page of the Prague Haggadah (woodcut from 1526)

# Mordecai Maisel

The surname Maisel is deservedly one of the most famous names among the Jews in Prague because there was no other person so charitable and modest, and never had any Jew done so much for his fellow-believers. It was he who had the muddy streets of the Jewish Town paved, and he also had the beautiful Jewish Town Hall built. Two synagogues, the Maisel-Synagogue and the High Synagogue are also reminders of his charity. The bath-house for women was also built through his generosity, as well as the poorhouse and the orphanage. The origin of such immeasurable wealth is revealed in the following legend.

Some two hundred years ago, a Primas[14] by the name of Jizchak was on his way back to Prague after a long journey. In the twilight the coachman lost his way in a dense forest. He drove on, once to the right, then to the left, over sticks and stones. Suddenly the horses shied, began to snort and reared up on their hind legs, scaring the coachman and the Mayor travelling in the coach. As the two of them looked around for the cause, they caught sight of a small bluish light in the distance. Something flickered through the trees and gradually grew into a flaming mountain illuminating the entire surroundings. Rabbi Jizchak, a fearless and hearty man, had the eyes of the horses blindfolded and went towards the place where the flames were raging. As he approached, he saw two small dwarfs with long grey beards busily filling their sacks with gold and silver pieces from the glowing heap. They did not utter a word nor did they notice the newcomers. For a while Rabbi Jizchak silently watched them at work and then asked them: "Who are you filling the sacks for?" "Not for you", one of them answered angrily, then he and the gold and the sacks vanished. Only a few glittering pieces lay scattered on the ground. The other dwarf was friendlier and said: "It is for someone from your nation but with your question you have done harm to the treasure." Then he revealed that the treasure would be transferred after the wedding of his daughter. He also agreed that the Rabbi might exchange his money for the few golden pieces that were scattered on the ground. The Mayor took three pieces of gold from his purse, threw them on the ground, and picked up three pieces from the ground in exchange. At that moment everything

---

[14] Primas (in Latin: primus 'the first' ): the Mayor

vanished and there he stood, alone in the darkness. The Mayor returned to the coach and reassured the coachman that what they had seen was no more than burning piles of wood. Since the horses had calmed down again, they could now drive on. Before long the forest became thinner and thinner and the Mayor arrived in Prague by the dawn of the new day.

The curious Mayor could not make out who could be the unknown owner of such treasure and so he sought refuge in divine providence. He wrapped each of those pieces of gold in a scrap of paper and threw one of them out of the window onto the street. Despite the fact that the house was in a broad, busy street, the gold piece lay there unnoticed until the evening. Rabbi Jizchak had intended to have it brought up, when a cheerful, barefoot and poorly dressed boy appeared on the street. He hesitated in front of the rabbi's house, looked around anxiously and in a flash picked up the piece of gold and ran off. The Mayor shook his head thoughtfully and said: "What a fine millionaire!"

Dissatisfied with the Eternal God's whimsical provision, he could hardly wait for the following day to test destiny once more. But the same boy picked up the second piece of gold.

"It is strange," said the scholarly Mayor to himself. "Such an uncared-for boy! What is his connection to this? The Lord moves in mysterious ways, anyway!" On the third day the last piece of gold was thrown onto the street and indeed, the boy collected that one too! The wise Rabbi Jizchak was now convinced that this shabby-looking boy would one day get the great treasure from the forest. He wanted to know whether he really deserved so much wealth from the Lord. He had the town crier called and ordered him to announce the loss of the golden pieces with the request that the finder might reimburse them to the owner in accordance with the Law of Moses. In this way the Mayor hoped to discover both the character and the origin of the boy.

Shortly afterwards the boy appeared at the Mayor's house. He told him that he had come by the three pieces of gold in a most wondrous way. The night before, he had been told in a dream that he would make a discovery. Now he would like to return them to the owner in accordance with the Law of Moses. But he had only two pieces of gold since he had given one piece to his mother for her business. However, she would return it as soon as possible. Then the Mayor asked him with a smile: "You could have kept all three. Who would have betrayed you when no-one saw you? What a fool you are!"

For a moment the boy looked at him in astonishment, then said with devout ardour: "May the God of Israel prevent me from doing so. I would rather be poor and honest than make a fortune in an illegal way. Here are your pieces of gold."

His heart touched, the venerable Mayor approached the boy, put both hands on his head and said in a solemn voice: "May God bless you and be merciful unto you! You deserve to be a beloved child of our God. – Tell me, my son, would you like to stay with me? You would be happy in my house."

"Your Honour, I cannot do so," replied the boy. "I have an old blind father whom I have to care for while my mother goes about her business. Who would accompany him to the place of worship three times a day to say his prayers? No, I could not stay in your house even if you gave me your whole fortune. A stranger can never replace the devotion of a child. Above everything I prize the commandment: Honour your father and your mother, so that you may live long in the land."

The Mayor kindly asked the boy the name and profession of his father. When he found that it was Schalum Maisel and that he had worked as a carrier before he went blind, he gave both pieces of gold back to the boy and sent him home.

A few days later, the Maisel family were sitting at table and they discussed this event over and over again. Although the father praised the noble-mindedness of the Mayor, he thought that the rich have such moods and that they soon disappear like dreams. A man should not rely on the charity of the sons of the earth, as King David once said. And Mordecai, already fifteen years old would soon be able to attach a rope to his shoulders to carry loads and

A tombstone in the Old Jewish Cemetery

21

become a carrier like he himself and his father before him. He should be pious and righteous and then he would never lack God's blessing.

Then the door opened and the Rabbi Jizchak entered. After they had greeted each other, he sat down humbly and said that he had some things to discuss with the parents, and that meanwhile the boy could play outside with his friends. Then he asked father Maisel whether he would let Mordecai visit him because he would like to bring him up as his own son, and he would enable him to study. The embarrassed father objected that one should not trade in children, and that Mordecai was the last of his eight children. Rabbi Jizchak said quickly: "Just let me only finish what I have to say. You can keep your son with you; he will eat and drink at your home, but please let him come to my place for a few hours every day so that he can learn something and become a person of importance, because your son should not become a carrier," he said emphatically.

"I want him to become a competent and clever merchant. I am pleased with him and would like to give him the hand of my daughter Sulamit in marriage, if he keeps to his present path."

The two old people fell silent because they were not prepared for such an offer. Surely, had they known what the Mayor knew, that such a treasure was to be given to their son from the Almighty, they would most certainly have had even more objections. Filled with emotion the father could only say: "It has been decided by God that this plentiful blessing from heaven will come to him through your hands."

"We are therefore united," said Rabbi Jizchak and he rose from his seat. "For the moment it should remain only between ourselves. Neither your son nor my daughter should know of this matter until the right time comes. God be with you!" The Mayor went on his way and left the astonished parents alone with their pleasure.

Five years went by very quickly and pleasantly for young Maisel. During that time, his body gained in strength and beauty and his mind developed so much that he was considered the kindest, most charming and scholarly boy. His good heart remained unchanged in his love and helpfulness towards his poor parents. He was still taking his father three times a day to the synagogue and helping his mother in the small scrap metal business. Sulamit grew up and became even more beautiful, and Rabbi Jizchak noticed with paternal pride the growing affection between the two young people. When young Maisel was twenty years old and Sulamit turned sixteen, they got engaged.

There was uproar among the Jewish community in Prague over this extraordinary connection between the wealthy Mayor and the poor carrier. However, the Mayor let the people talk because he knew what he knew and after a year the loving pair were married in the yard of the Old-New Synagogue.

When all seven wedding days had passed, Rabbi Jizchak thought it high time to pick up the promised sacks of gold for his son-in-law. He had his carriage harnessed and, with Maisel, set out for a trip. They arrived at the forest in the evening, again at the place where the Mayor had had that miraculous experience six years before. They stayed there nearly all night and neither the glowing mountain, the dwarfs, the sacks of gold, nor the piles of gold appeared.

The disgruntled Mayor eventually turned back and was consoled only by the thought that it was not the right time yet.

Weeks, months and even a year elapsed; Rabbi Jizchak made several more trips to the mysterious place but in vain. The sacks of gold did not appear.

Finally, his belief in the miracle began to diminish and the Rabbi thought it must have been a spook or an evil spirit who wanted to lead him towards a connection so harmful to his dignity. Because of his disappointment, he became more sullen and bitter day by day and he treated his son-in-law with cold contempt.

Young Maisel, who had no idea of the expectations of his father-in-law, was so hurt by this unloving behaviour that he decided to set up his own houschold and not to eat the bread of charity nor live on the sufferance of his father-in-law any longer. When Sulamit agreed to this, the young pair left the paternal home and rented a dwelling for them-

selves. Maisel took over his mother's small scrap metal business and through his diligence he was able to turn it into an important store. Without the support of his father-in-law, he was able to provide for both his own household and that of his parents, and even saved up a little money. And so he lived, pleased with what the God of his fathers had given him.

As time passed, Maisel's house became a sanctuary for the needy and the oppressed. One day, when the generous Maisel was in his store, a peasant dressed in a smock came to the vault to buy some pieces of iron, or so he said.

After he had chosen what he wanted and gathered it together, he said: "Sir, I have no money now but I need the things urgently. If you would be so kind as to wait some time, I sincerely promise to pay you."

"If you need the things so urgently, I give them to you without payment. I don't know you but you will not deceive me. Go in the name of God and come again whenever you need something," said Maisel to him.

The peasant was visibly pleased by this and offered him a favourable deal. He said that for many years he had had a large iron box at home and that nobody was able to open it. He himself would never have any use for this iron box and he would sell it to the merchant after having it weighed. After the promise that he would get two kreutzers for every pound of usable iron, the peasant went away with his pieces of iron.

Three days later, he arrived in front of Maisel's iron-store in a coach bearing a huge box. The box was unloaded with great effort and put onto the scales. The sum was calculated and the peasant was delighted that after having paid all his debts, he even had a few florins left over for himself.

The following night, Maisel was about to try to open the box with a hammer and chisel. However, when tapped it the first time, it jumped open by itself. The astonished merchant saw that it was filled only with rolls of paper. He quickly unwrapped one of them and saw that pieces of gold were blinking at him. Silently, he took one roll after another and hid it in a secret place without telling anyone, not even his wife. He knew the weakness of women, who are unable to hold their tongues, even at a graveside.

Now Maisel was one of the richest Jews in the community but he was careful not to let the secret leak out to the public. The man might come back, Maisel thought, and his conscience refused to profit from a treasure that had come to him only through the innocence and ignorance of a peasant.

He waited for more than a year for the return of the peasant, about whom he knew absolutely nothing. But then he thought he must be entitled to use the treasure given to him from God.

He went to the Chief Rabbi and he said: "Sir! The God of Israel blessed the work of my hands and I have decided to build a house where His name shall be praised. Here is gold: invite the best master-builders to erect the most beautiful synagogue in Prague. But my name is not to be mentioned."

The devout Rabbi was surprised at the man's humility; he gave him his blessing and promised to do everything as he wished.

Finally, the masterpiece was finished; people came from near and far to visit the magnificent new temple and everybody praised the unknown benefactor who had financed it.

One feast day, the synagogue was consecrated. The elite of the town were present there and the Rabbi gave a heart-rending speech that ended with: "Blessed are you, O Israel! For you have such a good man in your midst! Step forward, you humble Saul! Why are you hiding among the crowd when you are really one of the greatest?" As he was talking, he pointed towards the corner where Maisel was hiding in embarrassment. "Step out of the darkness, you light of the Lord!" the Rabbi called excitedly. "You, Mordecai Maisel, I am calling you!"

When the people heard his name, a solemn silence spread through the crowd. It gradually changed into a gentle murmur and ended in loud jubilation. Countless hands raised the modest benefactor on high to bring him forward to the steps where the Chief Rabbi was standing. Full of humility, Maisel lowered his eyes, the Chief Rabbi quietly placed his hands on his head to bless him. Then he rose again and solemnly pronounced the blessing which ended with the plea: "May the foundations of this house remain undisturbed until one day through Your paternal benevolence Your children again assemble in the Temple of Jerusalem. Amen."

Rabbi Jizchak, who as Mayor occupied the seat nearest the Torah shrine, was beside himself with joy. As soon as the Chief Rabbi had finished and descended the steps, the rapturous father-in-law went up to his son-in-law and without a word pressed him to his chest. Everybody was pushing through the crowd to express their pleasure and their sincere good wishes to the delighted Mayor and his son-in-law. The people streamed happily from the temple to the house of the Chief Rabbi where a huge banquet was held for everyone without exception.

Mordecai Maisel remained a rich man for the rest of his life but he did not deviate from his piety and humility. He never accepted any function or title. His modesty is still praised among the Jews in Prague when they say:

"Maisel had no place reserved in the synagogue."

As an unknown donor he had to buy himself a place in the synagogue which he had financed. How much good he had done, we have just told. Even today you can read about his good deeds in the Maisel-Synagogue, in worn Hebrew verses engraved into the marble. His whole life was a chain of continuous good deeds.

Yet it is also said that the last hour of his life was not his best hour. On his death-bed, Mordecai Maisel told his wife to immediately give a large sum of money for the poor of the ghetto[15] to Rabbi Loew. Angrily, his wife refused to do so and thus embittered his last hour. After his death Mordecai Maisel's wealth vanished into oblivion. As Maisel had no children, the authorities declared his property invalid and ordered the confiscation of the entire legacy for their own purposes. There was a lot of bad blood during the court proceedings but Mordecai Maisel could know nothing of this any more.

---

[15] ghetto: enclosed separate district in Venice where the Jewish population was isolated from the rest of the population from 1516; districts where the Jews lived in other towns were also called ghettos later on

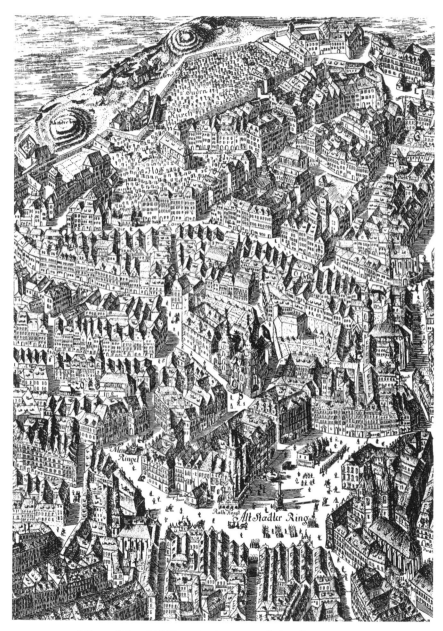

View of the Old Town in Prague and the ghetto (1769)

# The Quiet Jew

A tailor whose name was Reb Schime Scheftels lived in one of the poor houses in the upper part of the Jewish Town in Prague more than six hundred years ago. He was hardly able to provide for his wife and three children, and even his grandmother, the very old "Schammeste" Ziperl, had to help him a lot so that he and his family would not die of hunger. She also worked in the women's section of the Old-New Synagogue where she gave "assistance", especially to women who either had no experience with the rituals or were not literate. Schime Scheftels was not much respected because of his trade, neither did he have a particulary good reputation among the Prague Jewish community. He was not a learned man and could only learn a page of the "Gemara"[16] with difficulty. Everything in daily life not connected with his trade was distant and foreign to him. He loved only his wife and children, with a deep and quiet tenderness. Because of his calm nature he was soon nicknamed "the quiet Jew". Schime's shy and simple ways made him the target of ridicule, which he let pass without a word. His grandmother, however, could not ignore this happening to her grandson and shouted at the mockers repeatedly: "Leave my Schimele alone and remember – still waters run deep!" And she was right.

It was a June morning in 1286 of the common calendar. There was a hectic atmosphere in Prague's Jewish Town since it was the day before the Shavuoth holiday. Široká Street in the Prague ghetto was like a flower garden, as the women at the street stalls along the way from the Old-New Synagogue up to Golden Lane were selling flowers, nothing but flowers, for people to decorate their houses ready for the days of Shavuoth. Incredibly chaotic crowds

[16] Gemara: besides Mishnah the most important part of the Talmud

were pushing and shoving in the shops and narrow streets as they did the last shopping for the holiday. Suddenly this hubbub changed into a curious silence. A huge stocky man, holding a tall staff adorned with a large knob in his right hand, accompanied by a gang of children, came along Rabbi Street. It was Reb Leser, the town-crier of the Prague Jewish community. He stopped in the middle of Široká Street and hit the ground three times with his staff. There was a breathless silence for everyone knew that an important event was about to be announced. As soon as Reb Leser finished his announcement, which he had begun, as usual, with "Hört, liebe reboßaj"[17], it was quickly spread by word of mouth: "The King is coming!" Early that morning a courier had arrived in the Jewish Town Hall from Prague Castle and announced that King Wenceslas II[18] and his wife Judith would be coming to the Jewish Town to visit its curiosities.

After Reb Leser had made this news known in all the streets of the ghetto a real commotion broke out. The whole Jewish Town wanted to greet the King. Everything was being hastily prepared so as to give him a ceremonial welcome. The Minha prayer[19] had already been held in the synagogues at noon in celebration of the visit, and the representatives of the community gathered in front of the Town Hall a full two hours before the arrival of the King. In their midst was the Roschhakohol Reb Feiwel in official attire with mortarboard and buckle shoes, and Rabbi Jonathan, the Chief Rabbi of the Bohemian Jews, dressed in a silk coat and a tall fur-trimmed cap. The streets where the King was going to walk were full of people. The entire Prague ghetto was aglow with excitement.

When the bells of the Church of Our Lady of Týn announced the King's arrival at the gate of the Old-New Synagogue, jubilant cries filled the air, following the Royal couple wherever they appeared. In the Town Hall Square, their Majesties received homage from the representatives of the community. Then they visited the Old-New Synagogue and, cheered by the crowd, they set out on their return journey. Suddenly, the enthusiastic applause turned into horrified screams. From one of the houses in Beleles Street a brick fell down right in front of the King. Though uninjured, King Wenceslas left the place at once in a terrible rage. The Jewish community was seized by anxiety and fear because they knew

---

[17] courteous form of address (reboßaj is the plural form of rabbi) with an approximate meaning of: "My esteemed teachers, listen!"

[18] Wenceslas II [in Czech: Václav] (born 1271, died 1305): Bohemian King from 1278, the son of King Přemysl Otakar II

[19] an evening prayer

that this would have horrific consequences for all of them.

When the whole community gathered in the Old-New Synagogue for divine worship in the evening, Beth-din-Schammes[20], the servant of the Rabbinical college, brought the Chief Rabbi a letter with the Royal Seal. King Wenceslas ordered the Rabbi to notify the community that if the evil offender who had thrown the brick were not delivered to the authorities within eight days, the whole Jewish Town would be plundered and its inhabitants driven away on the ninth day. The entire community was terrified.

All efforts to find the guilty man immediately after the attack had been unsuccessful. Nobody was found in the house from which the brick had fallen. Everyone had been out on the streets watching at that time. It was suggested to the Royal authorities that the mishap might have been caused through carelessness during the reconstruction of the house, especially on the cornice. But this explanation was rejected. On the second day of Shavuoth holiday the Roshhakohol[21] asked for an audience with the State Chancellor of the King, whose name was Zawish of Rosenberg, but this was refused. He was

Student of the Talmud

[20] Schammes: a synagogal servant
[21] 'the head of the community'

told scornfully that the murderer must be at the Royal Castle before the five remaining days were up.

The Jews of Prague were in deep despair and they foresaw the end of their days. Rabbi Jonathan ordered three days of fasting and penance for the community after Shavuoth was over. They passed and still no solution had been found. The iron gates of the ghetto were now closed even during the day because the Jews were afraid of the fury of the mob, who were always ready to dress up their rapacity and hatred of the Jews as patriotic loyalty on such occasions. No Jew dared to leave the Jewish Town. Prayers of lamentation were said at the Old Jewish cemetery and in the synagogues, women lamented over the graves, clutching their children tight. Old Schammeste Ziperl sat in front of the Old-New Synagogue in deep misery, mumbling to herself: "The fathers ate sour grapes and children's teeth will be harsh."

On the 13th Sivan[22], after the eighth and last day, when the time limit for the Prague Jewish community had elapsed, a huge crowd of people waited in front of the gates of the Prague Jewish ghetto. Armed with axes, maces and other weapons, they were ready to start plundering immediately when the gate opened. The entire community gathered in the Old-New Synagogue. Only one person was missing – Reb Schime Scheftels, the "quiet Jew". He kissed his wife and his children as he always did, then left and did not come back. The community would surely not have noticed he was missing, had not his grief-stricken grandmother Ziperl been crying: "My poor quiet Schimele, what has happened to you?"

Weak murmurs of interest arose in the Jewish community, which was threatened by imminent disaster, when the news of the disappearance of the "quiet Jew" was brought in. Moreover, it was spread incredibly quickly after Rabbi Jonathan stepped onto the elevated Almemar[23] and ordered silence with a sweep of his hand. "The community has been saved from the imminent catastrophy," he declared, "but at what a price. One of us has, with few words, as always, sacrificed himself for the sake of Israel. Last night Reb Schime Scheftels, the "quiet Jew", went to the King's castle unbeknown to anyone and presented himself as the man who had tried to assassinate the King. We all know, however, that he is innocent and his memory shall stay sacred, as a sacrifice, in God's name. His sacrifice shall be accepted soon: the King has decided that Schime Scheftel is to die."

The happiness over the miraculous rescue turned into painful mourning. The heroism of the "quiet Jew" was an inexplicable miracle to the hearts of many people. But only one heart broke after the announcement. When old Schammeste Ziperl, who was sitting in

[22] Sivan: the ninth month in the Jewish calendar, it roughly corresponds with May – June
[23] Almemar, Almemor: a platform for the reading of the Torah

the women's section of the synagogue, heard that her grandson had saved the Prague Jewish community, she screamed for joy: "My dear quiet Schimele!" and fell over, dead.

The gates of the town were opened. Armed riders held back the mob that had wanted to invade and plunder the community. Their leader read out the King's Edict saying that the wrongdoer was now in hands of the King and the Jewish Town was free of the impending punishment. Furthermore, the culprit would be thrown down from the very house where he had committed his crime. Mounted mercenaries rode through the Old School Gate. In their midst was Reb Schime in chains, accompanied by Rabbi Jonathan. They stopped at the house in Beleles Street where the incident had taken place eight days before. The whole Jewish Town was gathered there. Not a single eye was dry when the humble tailor who had sacrificed himself for the sake of the entire community passed by without even looking up. He embraced his wife and his children and was led up onto the roof of the house which was to be his place of execution. The mounted soldiers were standing in front of the house with their pikes pointing upwards. Reb Schime turned once more to the east and then jumped onto the pikes shouting: "Sch'ma Jisraeel, adonoj elohenu, adonoj echod."[24]

For three long days the entire Prague Jewish community mourned their martyr; the Light of Soul burned for him in the Old-New Synagogue for ten days. On the third day after the death of the "quiet Jew" Rabbi Jonathan had a dream saying that Schime was a descendant of the prophet Zechariah who was killed by Israel because he protested against decadent customs.

Zawish of Rosenberg, State Chancellor of King Wenceslas II, died on the scaffold, guilty of high treason, two years after Reb Schimes had died a martyr's death. Fifteen minutes before his death he had Rabbi Jonathan from the Prague ghetto summoned and confessed that two years before he had instigated one of his servants to throw a brick at the King in a street of the Jewish ghetto. He knew this crime would be ascribed to the Jews. The Rabbi had to promise him that he would take care of the family of the "quiet Jew."

[24] The opening words of the Jewish confession of faith which proclaims the unity of God

Old butchers' shops in the Jewish Town in Prague

# Rabbi Loew's Engagement

In 1513 a son was born to the highly esteemed Rabbi Bezalel ben Chajim, a descendant of Raw Hai Gaon, an offspring of King David in the male line. The father, who was well known in the old town of Worms upon Rhine for his piety, named the child Jehuda Loew after a verse in the Bible. The child came into this world to protect the Jews against malicious defamation and suspicions on the Christians' part.

Some years passed. There were surely ample opportunities to master the rabbinical teachings in Worms. However, it was a practice of Jewish boys to keep faithfully the word given to their fathers to travel to far distant climes and to quench their thirst for knowledge at the feet of famous teachers and masters. Jehuda had hardly grown into a youth when he moved to Prague.

A rich and devout man called Reb Samuel Schmelke Reich, known as Rich Schmelke, was living in Prague at that time. When he decided that his virtuous daughter Pearl should be betrothed, his choice fell on Loew and he became engaged to Pearl at the age of just fifteen in accordance with the custom of that time. In order to fulfil the wish of Reb Schmelke, the young Loew soon moved to Poland to study at the famous School of Rabbi Sch'lomo Lurje in Lublin. He was at that time the head of the Jewish Diaspora and he shone as the brightest star in the skies of Jewish science.

Very soon after that Schmelke lost his fortune in an unsuccessful undertaking and so he was unable to provide the promised dowry or carry out the arrangements of the marriage. So he wrote to Loew, who had already reached the age of eighteen, telling him that he was not able to provide a dowry for his daughter. Therefore Loew did not have to feel bound to his vow; he would be forgiven and allowed to marry another woman.

Loew replied: "I trust in God's help, and I shall wait until He helps you to raise the funds for the dowry and for the wedding arrangements. Furthermore,

I will only consider the engagement broken if your daughter marries another man."

As the financial situation of Reb Schmelke was not improving, Pearl opened a store selling salt and bread and other groceries to help her elderly parents.

Almost a decade passed. Loew remained engaged; he did not get married but devoted himself to scientific study. For that reason, he was known as "Loew the Bochur"[25].

One day troops of soldiers happened to be in the streets of Prague. There was a high-ranking officer riding with them. As he was passing Pearl's store, he stuck his sword into the large loaf of bread that was used for display in the shop. Pearl was frightened and cried out. But she recovered immediately and asked the officer not to take her bread without paying for it because she had to feed her elderly parents from the meagre income from the store.

The officer took the saddle from his horse and threw it inside the shop saying: "I am hungry, but I have no money to pay for the loaf of bread, so take this saddle instead." With that he rode away.

Pearl was astonished when she picked up the saddle to find inside it a pile of golden ducats! She hurried home, and with tears of joy told her parents about the treasure she had been given in such a miraculous way.

Reb Schmelke realized then that the officer could have been none other than the prophet Elijah and that this new stroke of luck was owing to the merits of his son-in-law. Immediately he wrote to Loew that the heavens had sent him help in a miraculous fashion and asked him to come to Prague as soon as possible to celebrate his wedding.

Loew came to Prague and married his pious bride, and it was not long before he was summoned to be a Rabbi in Posen.

---

[25] Bocher, also bochur, bachur: a student of the Talmud, unmarried man

# Rabbi Loew, the Benefactor of the Jews in Prague

Rabbi Jehuda Loew ben Bezalel had worked in Posen for a long time when he was summoned to Prague Castle by Emperor Rudolph II[26]. There he was appointed Chief Rabbi of the Jewish Town, and he held this office until he died.

Rabbi Loew lived in Široká Street in the Jewish Town. Above the door of his house he had a lion with a grape engraved onto a stone to indicate his descent.

At that time, numerous Jewish immigrants from Russia and the Balkans settled in Prague and the town became a place of refuge for people from Spain and Portugal who were seeking asylum from the inquisition. Ordinary settlers from German towns also came, not least among them famous Talmudists.

At the time when Rabbi Loew settled in Prague, the Jews of Prague were once more threatened by great misfortune – they were to be expelled from the country. Rabbi Loew wanted to protect his people from this and he made appeals to the Emperor. When the valet rejected him, he looked for another way out of the predicament.

Rabbi Loew was waiting in the crowd of people who had gathered on the Stone Bridge to see the Emperor on his way to the Old Town. When he saw the imperial carriage approaching, he placed himself with arms outstretched towards the carriage. The spectators pelted the Rabbi with stones and pieces of excrement, yet he remained motionless, and then he saw and behold, the stones and excrement turned into roses and violets in mid-air.

The carriage stopped and the Emperor looked out of the window to see what was going on. The audacious Rabbi came closer, made a low respectful bow, handed the monarch his plea in writing and asked for an audience. The Emperor glanced at the list and ordered the petitioner not to leave his house for the following seven days.

[26] Rudolph II (born 1552, died 1612): legendary Bohemian King and Holy Roman Emperor from 1576

On the seventh day, a magnificent carriage appeared in front of Rabbi Loew's little house to take him to the Emperor.

Rabbi Loew sat with the Emperor and with other scholars and noblemen for a long time discussing the issues concerning the threatened expulsion. Rabbi Loew asked for the mercy of the law and for protection of the Jews in Prague.

On that very day Rudolph II ordered that no more injustice should be done to the Jews, that each of their offences must be tried before a court of law and that the whole community should never in future be held responsible for the guilt of an individual.

Many stories are told about the wisdom and ability of Rabbi Loew. His prestige increased day by day and before long it was said in Prague that he was as wise as Solomon[27] himself.

The favour of the Emperor did not last long, however, as he was mostly occupied with alchemy and astrology and left the affairs of the state to his advisers. They, however, did not want the Jews in Prague and they used every opportunity to incite the Emperor against them. Finally the Emperor, tired of all the never-ending quarrels and pressure from the ghetto, decided that all Israelites should be expelled from the country without delay.

The night after this decree was issued the Emperor had a very strange dream.

He saw himself in a carriage. The surrounding area was bare and shadowless and the Emperor was sweating, and could hardly breathe because of his thirst. Then he saw a river. He ordered the coachman to stop, got out of the carriage, undressed and stepped into the water to refresh himself. But when he returned to the riverbank he saw that his clothes, his carriage and his entire retinue had vanished.

The Emperor waited sadly for the onset of darkness before setting out for his castle. Under the protection of the darkness he walked the whole night and by daybreak he saw Prague in the distance. He met a group of woodcutters, but they insulted him and put the miserable Emperor to flight.

An old beggar gave him a few poor pieces of clothing so that he could go on his way. But then the monarch saw a fine carriage and he asked the man travelling inside the coach for help. He was abruptly rejected, however, and told that the Emperor was in his palace and that the man had just spoken to him.

It was suddenly clear to the Emperor what was going on. An impostor from his retinue had taken his clothes and his place and was impersonating him.

The Emperor brooded vainly about what to do. He wandered around the town the whole day and became more and more miserable. He was now also convinced that he had lost his power as well. Who would now believe that

[27] Solomon (born about 965 BC, died 926 BC): Ruler of the united kingdoms of Israel and Judea, the epitome of a wise and powerful ruler

there was a false Emperor sitting there in the castle and that he himself was not an impostor?

With sore feet and an empty stomach he came to the ghetto. He stopped in front of the Old-New-Synagogue and thought of Rabbi Loew. With his last strength he reached the Rabbi's house and was received with the greatest reverence. After he had washed himself, put on some clothes, eaten a little and rested a while, he asked the Rabbi for advice and help.

The Rabbi nodded his head and said: "Every criminal comes back to the place where he committed his crime. Today it will again by very hot and your double will undoubtedly go bathing. Where else would he be attracted to more than the riverbank, where he became Emperor by treachery? As he steps into the water, just do the same thing to him that he has done to you!"

The Emperor, feeling a new hope, promised the Rabbi all the treasure in the world.

But the Rabbi only said sadly: "If you want to give me something, do something else instead. Now you know the bitter taste of injustice. What you suffered in the filth and dust of the roads awaits our whole nation. Not just for a few hours but for the whole of our lives. Therefore I ask you to allow my nation to remain where we feel at home."

With great pleasure the Emperor issued a new decree annulling his resolution concerning the expulsion. Then he went to the River Vltava to await his double.

He had not long to wait. At the hour the Rabbi had announced, the imperial carriage appeared with his retinue. The impostor got out of the carriage, undressed and jumped in the water. At that moment, the Emperor stepped out from behind the hedge and ordered the coachman to go back to the castle as quickly as possible.

The horses ran as if possessed, the carriage was shaking from side to side over the rough road and then suddenly the Emperor woke up. He was lying in his own bed and then he realized that it had all been only a dream. He got up, went to the window and stood there for a long time deep in thought. When he returned to his bed, he glanced at his table – and stooped over it as if he had seen a mirage. On the table there were the rags given him by the beggar who had appeared in his dream and next to them a document compiled and signed by the Emperor.

He sat with his head lowered in contemplation for a long time. Early in the morning he passed the document with the decision about the annulment of the expulsion to his ministers. So Rabbi Loew was able to protect his loyal Jewish community from the hardship of expulsion.

Old post office in the Jewish Town

# The Wine Merchant and his Coachman

The famous Prague Rabbi Jecheskel Landau was sitting in his armchair in his study one day, frowning. In front of him on a long table were countless folio volumes. He was suddenly distracted by a loud creak as if someone had violently ripped open the door. Two men entered. The Rabbi recognized his countrymen by their traditional costumes (he came from Poland). He greeted them and welcomed them with "Scholem alejchem" according to their custom. After the usual questions: "Which country do you come from? Where are you going? What was your journey like?" the Rabbi asked what they wanted. They both began to speak at the same time and Rabbi Jecheskel had to ask one of them to be quiet while the other one spoke. Then, the first man started to tell his story:

"My name is Josef Kohen and I am the son of Simon Kohen, a wine merchant from Warsaw. This man's name is Chajim Geilis and I have employed him as my coachman for five years. In that time he has accompanied me on my business trips and he has behaved fairly and honestly. However, on the last Rosch-Chodesch[28] day, when I got up that morning (we had just arrived in Austria) I looked for my money sack and I soon found that it had disappeared! All my savings, a thousand ducats! So I called Chajim who is standing here as well, and asked him if he knew where my money was. He replied scornfully: "Where did you get so much money from in the first place?

You are still my coachman, aren't you? Did you rob someone?" At first I thought Chajim was joking (which he had never done before) and I told him to stop pretending. But I soon found that this absurd assertion had settled firmly in his head. He claimed with such certainty exactly the opposite of the truth: that I was his coachman and he was my employer. We have agreed to come and ask you, worthy Rabbi, whose wisdom is well known from one end of the world to the other, to determine who is the guilty one. But I, as the deceived, would like to ask you to help me get my thousand ducats back because I have a wife and child at home and the lost sum of money is my

[28] Beginning of a month, the first day of the month

entire life savings. The loss would make me and my whole family beggars." Josef Kohen kept on talking in this vein. When he finally finished, the Rabbi thought it over carefully and then asked Chajim to tell the story from his point of view. Chajim told the same story but with even greater emphasis and expressions likely to produce sympathy. He, Chajim, was the deceived one, and Josef Kohen the deceiver.

When they had both finished their stories, the wise Rabbi browsed through the folio volumes for a few minutes, as if it were written there which was the wine merchant and which the coachman. Suddenly he shut the books and appealed strongly to their consciences. But the hidden villain did not confess. However, Rabbi Jecheskel was a clever man. He thought of another way to loosen the tongue of the cunning deceiver. He asked both men to come

Ritual chalice from the time of Rudolph II

back at an appointed hour the following day. At the same time he ordered his servant not to let anyone enter his study unannounced.

The next day both Jews from Poland appeared at the Rabbi's house. As the servant went to announce them to the Rabbi, they stood waiting in the hall. The servant returned soon with a message for them to wait in the anteroom for a while because Rabbi Jacheskel Landau could not receive them yet. While they were talking to each other, the Rabbi rumbled along in his study, then all of a sudden he ripped the entrance door open quite unexpectedly and shouted in a harsh voice: "Come in coachman!" This was none other than Chajim, who was quite unprepared for this trick because he was usually called by that name; he fell into the trap and immediately entered the room in answer to the voice. There he was received by the rabbi with a thunderous dressing down. Chajim soon confessed his guilt, as there was no use in denying it any longer, and returned the stolen thousand ducats.

Word of this successful trick spread quickly throughout the entire Jewish community. There were crowds in the streets to see the two Jews from Poland who had become famous through no merit of their own. This incident had the greatest influence on the Chief Rabbi's opponents, however, who, after Rabbi Landau proved his wisdom and reasonable caution, laid down their arms and became his best friends.

Not only Prague but the whole of Bohemia rejoiced when the story of this clever ruse, which had uncovered the truth so quickly, reached the public. Wherever there was a small gathering of Jews at that time, nobody spoke of anything but Rabbi Chaskele Jampolis (who was known by this name because he was often called that in his homeland) and his encounter with the two Polish Jews. This event may have been small and distasteful in itself but it established forever the Rabbi's reputation for superior wisdom, which he then proved in many cases, during the forty years he was in office in Prague. Long after that old people from Prague who had personally known the Chief Rabbi could often be heard to say: "Der Zadik war ein Nizuz von Schlomo hamelech."[29]

From that time on Rabbi Jecheskel Landau lived in undisputed peace in his community and later, when his works such as "Nodabijhuda" and "Zlach" were published, he became famous far and wide among Talmudic scholars.

---

[29] "That devout man was a spark of Solomon's wisdom."

A street in the Prague Jewish Ghetto

# Beleles Street

In the time of Emperor Rudolph II a plague suddenly broke out among the Prague Jews, which, sparing the adults, only claimed children. The Angel of Death raged terribly in the homes of the people of Israel. Hundreds of dead bodies were taken to the Beth Chajim[30] every day, even every hour. The corpses had to lie there for days before they could be buried. There were not enough hands to dig the graves for the poor little children who had been taken away before their time. And the poisonous fumes from the unburied bodies served only to increase the plague.

The community was beset with misery and lamentations. As the Black Death had developed only in the Jewish Town, it soon became clear that the whole community was being punished for an unknown crime committed among the Jews. Special prayers were said and days of fasting were ordered to expiate for their sins and to beg Heaven for the lifting of the plague. The gravediggers were still continually busy. All the Rabbis and learned men from Prague met to discuss how to stop the raging of the Angel of Death.

First the Rabbis tried to find out what had caused the plague; what crime had brought such a punishment upon the entire community. Yet nobody seemed able to give a reason for it.

The Chief Rabbi Loew, who had taken part in the conversations, thought long and deeply in his bed the night after the first fruitless discussions. He eventually fell asleep and had a vivid dream. It was midnight and the prophet Elijah[31] came to him and led him to the Beth Chajim, where the bodies of the children rose up from their graves. The Rabbi awoke, and pondered about his dream for a long time. It seemed to him that it was God's inspiration on how to get to the root cause of the plague. So he called one of his most courageous disciples and told him: "God, our Lord, has sent misery and misfortune to us because we have

[30] Beth Chajim: the House of Life – the Old Jewish Cemetery in Prague
[31] Elijah: "My God is Jahweh"; an Israelite prophet who revealed Jahweh's claim to exclusivity in the first half of the 8th century BC

sinned heavily. In order to find out which crime are we guilty of, muster your courage and go to the Beth Chajim around midnight tonight. When you see the dead children rising from their graves in white shrouds, rip one Tachrichim[32] off and bring it to me."

The disciple did what he was told. He went to the cemetery around midnight and, filled with anxious expectation, waited to see what would happen. He had been waiting for perhaps half an hour when he heard the clock on the Jewish Town Hall strike twelve. And immediately, there was life under the tombstones. Small children in white shrouds emerged and, floating above the graves, they began a bizarre ghostly dance. A fit of shivering seized the disciple and all his limbs trembled as he watched this eerie performance. But the well-being of the Jewish community depended on his courage and so he ripped off the shroud from one of the children and hurried away.

Quite out of breath he arrived at the house of the Rabbi Loew. He told him what he had seen and gave him the shroud of the dead child. Soon after that the Rabbi saw the ghost of a naked child floating nearby. The children had carried on dancing in the cemetery. At one hour after midnight all of them scurried back to their graves again. Only then did the child notice that its shroud was missing, without which it could not enter the tomb. It ran quickly to the Rabbi's house and stopped in front of the window. It stretched out its hands and cried, begging and weeping: "Rabbi, give me my Tachrichim!" But the Rabbi held the shroud tightly and said: "If you want your Tachrichim, then first of all you must tell me the real cause of this plague."

At first the ghost of the child said nothing but continued to cry over the lost shroud. The Rabbi remained resolute and in the end the little ghost revealed the reason for the plague. Two husbands living in a street not far from the house of Rabbi Loew had indulged in an immoral exchange of their wives. That was why the whole community had been punished by the Black Death. It would not end until the two couples were punished. "And now that I have told you the reason for the plague, give me back my Tachrichim!" said the ghost. The Rabbi returned the little shroud and then the ghost went off happily with the Tachrichim to the Beth-chajim to rest in its grave again and enjoy eternal sleep. The two couples who had brought such a great misfortune and misery on the community were strictly punished and the plague was over.

The street where the two couples had lived began to be called by the people Beleles Street: one of the women who had committed the sexual offence was called Bella, and the other one was called Ella.

---

[32] Tachrichim: the shroud

# The Creation of the Golem

It was the year 1580. A priest called Thaddeus – a fanatical anti-Semite – tried again to disrupt the peace and harmony and to bring about discord and disharmony and provoke new superstitious accusations of blood rituals.

Rabbi Loew soon learned about it and raised a question "upwards" in his dream to find a solution to the problem of how he should fight against this evil enemy.

He received the following alphabetically arranged answer in reply:

"Ata Bra Golem Dewuk Hachomer W'tigzar Zedim Chewel Torfe Jisrael."

"You shall create a Golem from clay, that the malicious anti-Semitic mob be destroyed."

Rabbi Loew interpreted the line of strange words to mean that he should create a living body from clay with the aid of the letters provided from heaven.

He called for Jizchak ben Simson, his son-in-law, and for one of his disciples, Jacob ben Chajim Sasson, the Levite[33], and entrusted them with the mystery of how a Golem could be created. "Therefore I ask for your help because for the creation of a Golem, four different elements are required. Jizchak, you are the element of fire; Jacob, you are the element of water and I myself am the element of air. Together we shall create a Golem from the fourth element, which is the earth."

Then he told them in detail how they must first sanctify and purify themselves through deep and serious repetance in order to be ready for the great work of creating a Golem.

On a fixed day the three men went to the Mikveh (the ritual bath) after midnight. This time they bathed with special devotion and then went home without a word. At home they performed Chazot, the midnight lament for Jerusalem, prayed and chanted the relevant psalms. Finally they went to the bank of the River Vltava. There they looked for a place where clay could be found and set to work immediately.

Chanting the psalms by torchlight they began to work with feverish haste.

[33] An Israelite tribe (Old Testament) named after Levi, the son of Jacob and Leah

They kneaded and shaped a human figure with all its limbs from clay, measuring three ells in length. And there was a Golem lying in front of them with his face pointing towards the heavens.

The three men then stood at his feet so that they could see his whole face.

He lay there as motionless as a dead body.

Now Rabbi Loew ordered Jizchak, the priest, to walk seven times around the clay mass starting from the right side. He also entrusted him with the Zirufim, the formula combining the words that he should say as he walked.

By the time this was finished, the clay body glowed as red as fire.

Rabbi Loew asked Jacob, the Levite, to walk just as many times around the Golem starting from the right, and the specific Zirufim for his element was indicated to him. When the second assistant had finished his task the fiery red faded and water streamed into the clay body; hair began to appear on its head and also the nails began to grow on its fingers.

Then Rabbi Loew himself walked around the Golem and inserted a Schem[34] written on parchment in the Golem's mouth. Then all three of them bowed towards the east, the west, the south, and the north, and said in unison the following words: "And the Lord formed the man from the dust of the ground and breathed into his nostrils the breath of life, and the man became a living being."

The three elements – fire, water and air – caused the fourth element, the earth, to become alive. The Golem opened his eyes and looked around in amazement.

And Rabbi Loew said to him: "Get on your feet!" and the Golem stood up.

Then they dressed him in the garments of a synagogal servant and he soon looked like a common man. Although he could not speak, this later turned out to be an advantage.

At daybreak four men went home.

On the way, Rabbi Loew said to the Golem: "We have created you from a lump of clay. Your mission is to protect the Jews from persecution. Your name will be Josef and you will live in the Rabbi's house. Josef, you must obey my commands no matter when and wherever I might send you – into fire, into water, to jump from a roof or even to the seafloor."

Josef nodded his head and made movements to show his approval.

At home Rabbi Loew said that he had met a dumb stranger on the street and that he felt compassion for him, so he had brought him to his house as a servant.

But he prohibited the people in the house from using the Golem for their private purposes.

---

[34] Schem: from 'Schema' – name. In this case, the name of God

# The Torah Scroll that Fell

It happened that on the Day of Atonement in 1587 in the Old-New Synagogue, when Rabbi Loew was at his prayers, a leader of the community dropped the Torah scroll[35] when he was about to return it to the Holy Ark following the afternoon reading. The incident caused consternation among the members of the community assembled there because this was always considered to be a bad omen. Rabbi Loew was also upset and immediately ordered that all persons present should fast the following day. On Monday night he raised a question in his dream as to what sins would have caused such a distressing incident. He did not get a clear reply but received an answer consisting of written characters that he did not know how to interpret. So he wrote the characters on a piece of paper and gave it to the Golem with instructions to find out the answer.

When the Golem had taken a look at the piece of paper, he immediately took the book of prayers from a bookcase, opened it and pointed to that section of the Torah that is read in the afternoon on the Day of Atonement. The letters that were shown to Rabbi Loew were the abbreviation of the verse: "Do not have sexual relations with your neighbour's wife and defile yourself with her."

Rabbi Loew knew then that the man who dropped the Torah was having an adulterous relationship and that was why the scroll had slipped from his hands. He invited the man to his house and told him privately about the reply that he had received in his dream. Then the weeping man confessed his sins and asked the Rabbi to impose a penance on him.

However, Rabbi Loew went even further – he arranged the divorce of the adulterous wife from her husband in accordance with the Law of Moses.

---

[35] Torah: originally 'Teaching' – the Bible; later the entire book of the Jewish religious teaching

Rabbi Loew and the Golem

# The Golem is Enraged

Rabbi Loew established the custom of giving a sort of daily plan to the Golem every Friday afternoon because he did not want to speak to him on the Sabbath except for extremely urgent reasons. Normally, Rabbi Loew would order him not to do anything else on the Sabbath but be on guard.

Once Rabbi Loew forgot to give his daily plan to the Golem on Friday afternoon. And so the Golem had nothing to do.

Almost as soon as the sun had set and the people were preparing themselves for the arrival of the Sabbath, the Golem began rampaging around the Jewish Town like a madman, wanting to demolish everything that got in his way. His inactivity had made him both frightend and angry. When the people saw him, they fled shouting: "Josef Golem has gone crazy!"

There was a terrible panic and the news soon reached the Old-New Synagogue where Rabbi Loew was at prayer. He ran out and without seeing the Golem he yelled: "Josef, stop it!"

Then the people saw how the Golem stopped, motionless, right on the spot where he was. At that moment all of his ferocity had vanished.

When the Rabbi was told where the Golem was standing, he went there and whispered in his ear: "Go home and lie down in bed!" And the Golem followed him as willingly as a child.

Then Rabbi Loew went to the synagogue again and told the congregation to sing the Sabbath hymn once more. After that Friday he never again forgot to give his daily plan to the Golem because he knew that the Golem would have been capable of devastating the whole of Prague had he not quietened him in time.

The Old Jewish 'Beth Chajim' Cemetery in Prague

# The End of the Golem

A long time had passed and the community was no longer threatened by any malicious accusations. Rabbi Loew summoned his son-in-law Jizchak and his disciple Jacob, the Levite. Both had participated in the creation of the Golem, and he told them: "The Golem has outlived his purpose as there are no accusations of blood rituals to fear any more. Therefore we shall send him from this world."

It was the beginning of the year 1593. Rabbi Loew ordered the Golem not to spend that night in the Rabbi's house but to take his bed to the loft of the Old-New Synagogue and spend the night there. This happened in secrecy since it was about midnight.

Two hours after midnight, Rabbi Loew's son-in-law, and Jacob, the Levite, came to the house of Rabbi Loew. The question of whether a dead man like the Golem could be regarded as an unclean object like other dead bodies was raised. This was a very important question because otherwise the priest would not be allowed to assist at the Golem's destruction. However, Rabbi Loew decided that this was out of the question. The three men, accompanied by a servant, climbed up to the loft where the Golem was sleeping.

They began the process of destruction. They did everything they had done when creating the Golem, only in reverse. If they had placed themselves at the Golem's feet looking into the Golem's face during the process of creation, then now they stood at his head. The words from Genesis were read backwards. After this had been done the Golem was transformed again into the mass of clay he had originally been. Then Rabbi Loew called the servant, took the candles and told him to undress the Golem except for his shirt. He should also burn the clothes without being seen. The stiff Golem was then covered with old prayer shawls and with the rest of the books that were kept in the loft of the synagogue in accordance with Jewish custom.

In the morning it was announced in the streets of the Jewish ghetto that Josef Golem had fled the town during the night. Only a few people knew the truth. Rabbi Loew proclaimed in all the synagogues and in all the houses of prayer that it was strictly prohibited to enter the loft of the Old-New-Synagogue and that the remnants of books and sacred objects were not to be kept there ever again.

A tombstone in the Old Jewish Cemetery

# Rabbi Loew and the Rose

The following legend reveals how Chief Rabbi Loew once saved his own life thanks to his wisdom.

The Prague Jewish community was suffering from the Black Death again. This time it left no one untouched, affecting young and old people alike. The bodies piled up in the Beth Chajim as there were neither enough gravediggers nor enough space to bury them. Rabbi Loew was almost a hundred years old at that time, and his hair and beard were as white as snow. He searched in vain in his books of learning for the cause of all this misery and what should be done to heal it. In the greatest distress, he remembered his dream from the time of the terrible children's plague. Accompanied by his bocherim and the synagogal servants he went to the small rear gate of the cemetery at night.

As he was about to take the key, the door opened and a tall, pale, thin man stepped out. He held a tremendously long paper list in his hand. The wise Rabbi immediately recognized the man who was standing before him – it was Death. Rabbi Loew snatched the list from his bony hand. On it were the names of those who were to die the next day including that of Rabbi Loew and those of some of his companions. The Rabbi was frightened and tore the list into small pieces.

"You have escaped this time," said Death, "but take care to keep away from me a second time!"

Rabbi Loew took heed of this warning. For he knew that Death would be waiting at every corner to outwit him. He took up his books again. And as he was also knowledgeable in mechanics, he created a small device to protect him and always carried it with him. If Death appeared somewhere nearby, the device began to tinkle softly as would an old clock, and the Rabbi, could escape him.

Death hid in a variety of shapes to catch the Rabbi but the wise Talmudic scholar noticed him every time. The Grim Reaper once took on the appearance of a pedlar-woman, next time he came as a fisherman offering fish for

Sabbath. Then as an old beggar, as a bocher or as an elegant gentleman who wanted to pay his respects to the Rabbi. But the Rabbi's protective device always warned him in time against any mortal danger.

Many years passed and it was the Rabbi's birthday again. All his disciples, relatives and friends gathered at the Rabbi's house to show him their esteem and gratitude.

The Rabbi was so touched by these expressions of appreciation that he left his device in his study. He walked towards his guests with a friendly smile. His youngest granddaughter came to him last and gave him a beautiful rose. The Chief Rabbi accepted this fragrant gift with pleasure and smelled it. At that very moment, he collapsed because Death had been hiding in the rose.

The magic device was tinkling with an almost silver tone in the adjacent room, but in vain. It rang for a long time until its spring broke, then it stopped forever. No one had noticed that a small dewdrop was on one petal of the rose in which Death had come.

The tombstone of the Chief Rabbi is situated near the west wall of the Old Jewish cemetery. He rests there with his wife in a temple-like sarcophagus. His tombstone is marked with a carved lion. The gravestones of thirty-three of his favourite bocherim stand in a long line to the left and right of Rabbi Loew's tomb.

A cemetery impression

Portal of the Jewish Town Hall in the Prague Ghetto

# Pinkas Street

A poor Jew lived in Prague more than two hundred years ago. During the day, just to keep body and soul together, he would walk through the streets with a bundle on his shoulder and buy up old clothes. At night, however, he studied law in his poor abode by the light of a dim lamp. Despite his diligence his earnings were far from enough to cover his family's expenses, and he, together with his wife and child, would have starved to death had it not been for a kind-hearted nobleman who had given him his support. He told his protégé to show him each Friday how much he had earned during the week. When it was not enough to celebrate Sabbath in keeping with the rules and the law, the nobleman made up the rest. Pinkas — this was the name of the Jew — was told to inform the nobleman, prior to other feasts, about the necessities required for those feast days, and then he received money for them.

Poor Pinkas considered the kind-hearted nobleman to be an angel from God. Therefore the way in which he thanked his benefactor was more of a prayer to God than an acknowledgement of the charity he had received. Each time he was given a gift by the nobleman he looked up to heaven and said: "God, you do not abandon your children and you have helped me again!" When the nobleman asked him after the feast days how he had spent the time, he always answered: "Oh, God has helped us!"

This behaviour irked the nobleman. He said to himself: "These people are so ungrateful! I overwhelm the Jew with good deeds to help him celebrate his Sabbath and he always says that God has helped him. We'll see if God helps him if I withdraw my support and deny him the usual gifts now, as Passover[36] approaches." There were a

[36] Passover: "When the Lord goes through the land ... he will pass over that doorway, and he will not permit the destroyer to enter your houses and strike you down." (Exodus 12:23) A feast to commemorate the exodus of the Israelites from Egyptian bondage

few days left before the beginning of the holiday when every faithful Jew must provide himself with food for the following eight days. For the past few years Pinkas had been receiving money for the most essential things from the nobleman. But this year his patron wanted to leave it to God's help and when he was humbly reminded by the Jew of the approaching holiday he said: "My dear Pinkas, you must provide yourself for the Matzoth[37] alone this year. I am in difficulties these days. Money has not been coming in and I've had great expenses. Your God will help you in another way." A shadow of sadness appeared on Pinkas' face when he heard these words from his benefactor. Yet he did not lose his firm trust in the God of his fathers. He said sadly but calmly: "Never mind. God will help us!" and he went away. With a sorrowful heart he came home in the evening. His wife, who was waiting impatiently, and the children, who had been looking forward to the promised clothes, met him with hurried questions. "How much did you get this year?" asked his wife. "I haven't got anything," answered her husband sadly, threw his empty sack in the corner of the room and prepared himself for evening prayer. The disappointed wife was nagging, the children were crying and poor Pinkas was worried. Crestfallen, he went back to his little chamber, locked the door behind him and studied law undisturbed, by the light of the gloomy lamp, until midnight.

Midnight had not yet passed. The children slept on their paltry straw mattresses and his wife also fell asleep, moaning. Pinkas sat alone over a large folio volume, stroking his long beard thoughtfully and staring in front of him fixedly, trying to interpret a difficult, contradictory part of the Talmud. All of a sudden, the small window blew open and its shutters rattled. A hideous body burst into the chamber and fell down at Pinkas' feet. Pinkas jumped up aghast, took the thick book and held it in front of himself as a shield, while his trembling lips were saying a formula against evil spirits. At that moment the laughter of many voices could be heard. This only confirmed the Jew's conviction that Masikim (evil spirits) had come to torment him. He kept holding the book in front of him, remaining in that position until his wife, awakened by the noise, knocked on the locked door of the chamber. This gave courage to her frightened husband. He tentatively glanced over the Talmud and saw a grimace similar to that of a man, and limbs stretched out in front of him. This repulsive spook was a dead monkey. Since Pinkas had his own strange views about monkeys, this vision only increased his fear. He considered these animals to be half human, kept by the noblemen and taken care of so that they would

---

[37] Matzoth, Mazzes: unleavened bread for Passover ('bread of affliction'); a symbol commemorating the exodus from Egypt that happened so quickly that the bread could be baked only like this

become moral and blessed. In his eyes, such a tame learned monkey was the same as a Christian Proselyte[38]. The frightened Jew started to ponder over all the sad events of the last year.

"They will come now," he said, "to drive me and my brethren from this earth. They will say that I killed this thing here. You, good Lord in heaven, please, take pity on me, a poor man!" Meanwhile the anxious, frightened wife tore the door open violently and asked what had happened. When her husband told her everything, she cried out: "Yes, it is a trick to ruin us. We have to get the dead animal out of the house at once." "But how, and where to?" asked Pinkas. "Should I wrap it up and throw it into the water? I could easily fall into the hands of a catchpole, and apart from that am I not strong enough to carry the dead body away." After a long discussion about this matter, Pinkas suddenly cried out in a

[38] Proselyte (from Greek 'the one who converts'): someone who changes from one party or religion to another one; in Antiquity especially pagans who joined Jewish communities

Signet of a Jewish printer's family in Prague (1603)

happier voice: "Do you know what we shall do? We shall burn the half man. Go on, light the fire and I shall bring in wood." A good strong fire was made in the stove and then Pinkas and his wife took the monkey's feet to drag it to the kitchen. As they were dragging it, there was the sound of a coin rolling on the floor. They dropped the dead monkey and followed the sound. Pinkas took a lamp, his wife a pine spill, and they searched the floor eagerly. How happy they were when they caught sight of a ducat glittering in the corner! They grabbed the dead monkey once more with much greater courage and they tried to drag it farther along. And what a surprise! Gold coins fell from the animal's throat. Pinkas looked upward and cried in a tone of devotion: "I was young and I have grown old and I have seen neither a pious man abandoned nor his children looking for bread." He took a big knife and started to dismember the animal. He was looking for the source of the money and he soon found it. The stomach of the animal was full of ducats. Pinkas removed them. When there were none left he cut the heaven-sent animal into small pieces and burnt them on the stove. The gold coins were cleaned and put in a bag. The floor was scoured clean and all traces of blood removed. By dawn there was no sign of the monkey, except the coins which were in the delighted Pinkas' bag.

"What you spend on glorification during the Holy days will be richly re-warded by the Lord!" says the Talmud. Poor Pinkas provided everything his wife desired – clothes for the children, spotless linen and richly embroidered hoods. Neither were delicacies, relishes and beverages, such as the best wine and the finest meat, missing. Prosperity and pleasure prevailed in the home where just the day before there had been the direst need. Passover had not been celebrated in such a joyful way, and with such piety and prayers, since the Exodus of the Children of Israel from Egypt, as it was at the Pinkas house at this time. An eight-branched chandelier above the table and wall-lights with polished round shades dispersed bright light throughout the clean, warm room. Next to the table was an upholstered couch decorated with large flowers. This was for the head of the household who was stretched out on it in full length, wrapped in a shroud. The lady of the house sat opposite her husband. She was dressed in a long richly folded spencer and had a bonnet decorated with stiff lace and wide silken ribbons. She was filling the glasses with wine. The children sat around the table with happy faces, waiting impatiently for what was to come. On the table stood a round pewter bowl containing three Matzoth wrapped in a large cloth. Horseradish, cress, baked eggs, a joint of roast meat and a container of salted water were also there. The bowl was raised by the people around the table, who said the following verses: "This is the bread of affliction, which our fathers ate in the land of Mizrajim[39]. He who is hungry come, eat with us." Suddenly there was the sound of a carriage. Before Pinkas could finish what he was saying someone knocked on the window.

Pale from fright Pinkas rose from his couch to find out who had disturbed them. He asked with a trembling voice who was at the window. "Open the door, Pinkas! I have come to celebrate Passover with you today!" a voice replied. At first they thought that the latecomer was none other than the prophet Elijah, who visited pious people at this time. For this reason there must be a glass specially filled for him on the table. The bar was removed quickly, the door opened and the nobleman, Pinkas' patron, came in. "Do not let me disturb you at your prayers. But – what do I see!" he exclaimed looking round the room in amazement. "Have you suddenly become a rich man?" "Yes," said the Jew laughing. "God the Almighty has helped me. A few days ago I was very poor and had no idea how I might celebrate this Passover properly, as every Jew is expected to do. However, God helped me and I am a rich man now." "Would you mind telling me," the nobleman said, "how your situation change happened so quickly?" "No," answered Pinkas and related the true story to his patron, who listened attentively. When the Jew mentioned the monkey,

the nobleman could no longer conceal his astonishment and exclaimed: "What! A dead monkey? It must have been mine. That is incredible! My monkey passed away suddenly three days ago. I had it taken from the house I did not want to see it anymore. Nevertheless, what does this have to do with your good fortune?" When Pinkas heard these words, he went to a box and unlocked it. He took out the large pouch and handed it to the patron saying: "Everything except the few coins that I spent in order to celebrate the Holy day is there." "What do you mean?" asked the nobleman in amazement. "Well, the monkey had the gold inside its stomach. But as the monkey belonged to you, so does the gold," answered the Jew. Then the nobleman turned to his servant who was standing a short distance away. He asked: "Do you happen to know more details about this story?" "Forgive me, my lord," replied the terrified servant, "the house servant wanted to play a prank on poor Pinkas. He threw the animal into his chamber. Several other servants knew about it." "What! The house servant? The prank turned out surprisingly," said the nobleman, smiling. "I had the poor boy put in jail despite his innocence. However, let it be a penalty for the crime he committed against poor Pinkas. The foolish animal probably wanted to imitate me and ate the gold, which I missed from my desk.

[39] Mizrajim: a Hebrew name for Egypt

Inhabitants of the Prague Ghetto

The monkey saw that I put the lighter coins between my teeth to mark them and thought that they were edible!" "The gold is here," Pinkas interrupted him, and passed the pouch over to his patron. "No, my honest Pinkas. The God of your fathers gave you this treasure and it shall be yours. I refused to give you the usual donation this year to see if God would really help you without me. You always kept saying: God has helped me. I understand now that your confidence in Him is justified. I shall spend this evening with you," he said. "So do not let yourself be disturbed and continue as if I were not here. My wife shall come soon and learn about this miraculous coincidence." The carriage was indeed sent away and in a short time the nobleman's wife arrived. Both of them stayed on until Pinkas ended the Seder[41] with the verse: "One day God will destroy the Angel of Death!"

Within a few years, Pinkas had used his diligence, wisdom and the nobleman's money to gain great wealth. His honesty and wisdom increased his reputation among the people, and soon he was elected the Mayor of the Jewish community. Nevertheless, he was always honest and humble just as he had been when poor. His house was a meeting place the for wisest Rabbis. His hand was open to everyone who was in need and the hungry poor people ate at his table every day. He had several dwellings built for the poor in the street where he lived. A magnificent synagogue was erected at his expense, which still carries his name today. And that street is called Pinkas Street.

---

[41] Seder: a section from the Bible or the Talmud; a name for the evening of Passover when the Haggadah is read

The legends have been taken from the following sources:

Sippurim. *Prager Sammlung Jüdischer Legenden in neuer Auswahl und Bearbeitung.* Vienna and Leipzig, 1926.

Bloch, Chajim. *Der Prager Golem.* Berlin, 1920.

Klutschak, Franz (ed.). *Das Panorama des Universums zur erheiternden Belehrung für Jedermann und alle Länder.* Prague, 1843.

A supplement to *"Ost und West".* Prague, 1843.